TITLES AVAILABLE FROM LAGOON BOOKS:

MIND BENDING PUZZLE BOOKS

MIND-BENDING LATERAL THINKING PUZZLES	(ISBN 1899712062)
MORE MIND-BENDING LATERAL THINKING PUZZLES (VOL II)	(ISBN 1899712194)
MIND-BENDING CONUNDRUMS & PUZZLES	(ISBN 1899712038)
MIND-BENDING CLASSIC LOGIC PUZZLES	(ISBN 1899712186)
MIND-BENDING CLASSIC WORD PUZZLES	(ISBN 1899712054)
MIND-BENDING CROSSWORD PUZZLES	(ISBN 1899712399)

FANTASTIC OPTICAL ILLUSIONS & PUZZLES	(ISBN 1899712402)
WHERE IN THE WORLD AM I? - MYSTERY GEOGRAPHY PUZZLES	(ISBN 1899712410)
AFTER DINNER GAMES	(ISBN 1899712429)
MIND-BOGGLERS	(ISBN 1899712445)
PUB TRIVIA QUIZ	(ISBN 189971250X)
60 SECOND MURDER PUZZLES	(ISBN 1899712453)

MYSTERY PUZZLE BOOKS

DEATH AFTER DINNER	(ISBN 1899712461)
MURDER ON THE RIVIERA EXPRESS	(ISBN 189971247X)
MURDER IN MANHATTAN	(ISBN 1899712488)
MURDER AT THRIPPLETON HALL	(ISBN 1899712496)

50 OF THE FINEST DRINKING GAMES	(ISBN 1899712178)

Books can be ordered from bookshops by quoting the above ISBN numbers.
Some titles may not be available in all countries. All titles are available in the UK.

Murder
at
Thrippleton Hall

A *Mystery*
PUZZLE BOOK

LAGOON
BOOKS

YOU ARE THE DETECTIVE!

Series Editor: Simon Melhuish
Editor: Heather Dickson
Author: Nick Hoare
Page design and layout: Gary Sherwood & Gary Inwood Studios
Cover design, photography & illustrations: Gary Sherwood

Published by:
LAGOON BOOKS
PO BOX 311, KT2 5QW, UK

ISBN: 1899712496

Printed in Singapore.

INTRODUCTION

You are a detective. Not just any old detective, but one with a fiendishly sharp mind, and an uncanny knack of being able to tie up even the messiest bird's nest of loose ends. You have been a detective for 20 years and have been waiting all this time to show the boys at the top just what you are really capable of. Now is your chance, the promotion you have always wanted is within your grasp...

There has been a death in the tiny market town of Thrippleton. Local toilet tissue magnate Orton Morton had been found dead. Having read reports of his suicide in the papers, you are initially puzzled as to why the police file has been passed to you. As you start to leaf through the file, however, you begin to see that this is not just another open-and-shut case of mid-life crisis. Far from it. The local police are sure it's murder but are clueless as to who did it. They need your help.

In the file are scene of crime reports, transcripts of interviews with each of the suspects, floor lay-outs of Thrippleton Hall and all the memos, letters and tip-offs the police have received since the fateful night.

Everything you need to crack the case is in the file. A murderer is loose and at last you've got an opportunity to show everyone what a great detective you are. What are you waiting for?

Index

USEFUL TIPS

- All the information *except the actual interviews with the six suspects* is 100% accurate, BUT it may not be relevant or particularly helpful.
- Remember that the murderer is not necessarily the only person who is lying. Other people may well have things they want to hide that are completely unconnected with the murder.
- The murderer acted alone. There may be many conspiracies, other characters may suspect or even feel fairly certain as to who killed the victim, but no-one knows for certain, apart from the murderer, of course.
- The local police, in the form of DS McGill, are fallible. If they weren't, they wouldn't need your help. Throughout the book there are times when McGill will assess the new developments. To stop yourself getting misled by these, and to make sure you are ahead of your rural rival, you should check your own conclusions before reading these. A notebook and pen might prove invaluable.

Remember, this is your case now and your promotion depends upon it.

Good luck!

FRAMPTONSHIRE CONSTABULARY

Thrippleton Police Station

M E M O

URGENT.

FROM: Chief Inspector T. Thomas

DATE: 20th July

RE: 'SUICIDE' OF ORTON MORTON

FOUL PLAY STRONGLY SUSPECTED.

ALL POSSIBLE SUSPECTS HAVE

BEEN INTERVIEWED BY OUR

OFFICERS.

ALL SCENE-OF-CRIME EVIDENCE

HAS BEEN COLLECTED

REGRET TO INFORM FAMILY THAT

LITTLE PROGRESS HAS BEEN MADE.

WE LACK NECESSARY

RESOURCES/SKILLS.

URGENTLY REQUEST ASSISTANCE.

REPEAT.

URGENTLY REQUEST ASSISTANCE.

YOURS FAITHFULLY

FThomas

CHIEF INSPECTOR THOMAS THOMAS

Scene of Crime Report 1

Date: 15th July

Offence: Suicide/Murder.

Victim: Orton Leigh Morton,
                   male, 61 years.

Perpetrator: Unknown.

Location: Thrippleton Hall,
                   Thrippleton, Westershire.

Description:
Body located in guest bedroom (first
floor). Found on floor (probably moved by
opening of door),with blood-stained fruit
knife 27cms from right hand. Chair
overturned. Suitcase upended on bed.
Clothes strewn over bed. Door hinges
damaged (probably on discovery of
crime). Window closed (unlocked). No other
signs of a struggle.

Cause of Death:
Loss of blood from neck wound, causing
fatal interruption of blood supply to the
brain.

First to Scene:
Felicity and Frank Morton

Time: 21:07hrs

Possible Suspects:

Quentin Morton (M) 26,
deceased's son, released from HMP
Whiteside on the day of the murder.
He served time for his role as accessory
in an armed robbery.

Felicity Morton (F) 57,
deceased's ex-wife, non-resident in
Thrippleton Hall, no previous convictions.

Frank Morton (M) 54,
deceased's younger brother, also non-
resident, no previous convictions.

Rebecca Morton (F) 29,
deceased's daughter, lives in Thrippleton
Hall, no previous convictions.

Damien Dawson (M) 31,
boyfriend of Rebecca Morton, non-resident,
no previous convictions.

Mathilde Lefarge (F) 35,
girlfriend of deceased, no record in UK,
applying to France for previous conviction
search.

Officer on Scene: DS Roger McGill

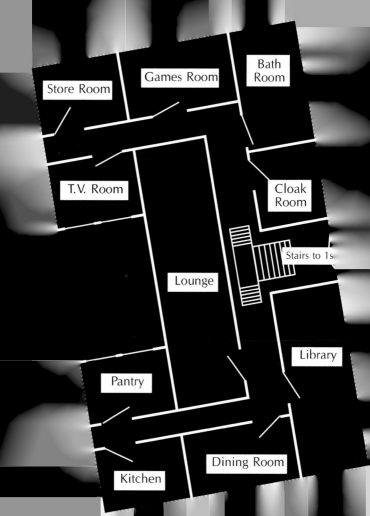

Store Room

Games Room

Bath Room

T.V. Room

Cloak Room

Stairs to 1s

Lounge

Library

Pantry

Dining Room

Kitchen

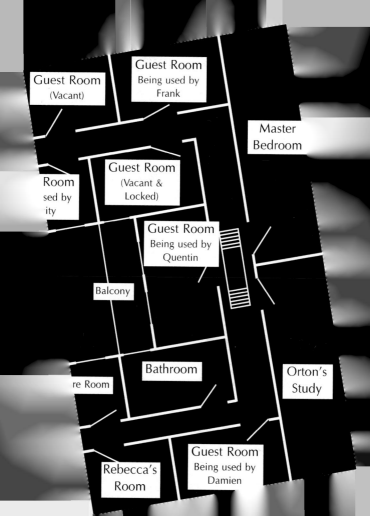

Quentin Morton
Age 26. Orton Morton's only son.

Expelled from the five most expensive schools in the country for a range of crimes including bullying, sheep worrying, drugs and joy-riding. Highly intelligent, yet incredibly destructive, he descended into an underworld of drugs and crime, adding accessory to armed robbery to his extensive record of petty theft, car crime and drug offences. He has just finished eighteen months of a three year sentence at HMP Whiteside, which was shortened by his impeccable behaviour whilst 'inside'. Immediately prior to his release, Dr Jeanette Williams, resident prison psychologist, said that, with one or two reservations, she considered him ready for rehabilitation into the community. The weekend of the 15th of July was the first face-to-face contact he'd had with his father for seven years.

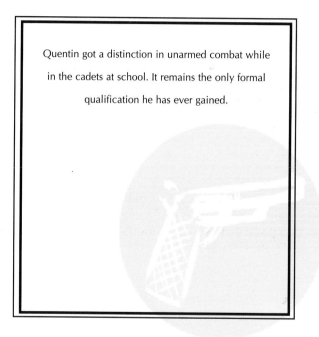

Quentin got a distinction in unarmed combat while in the cadets at school. It remains the only formal qualification he has ever gained.

Felicity Morton
Age 57. Orton's ex-wife; she was divorced from him 14 years ago.

After the separation she suffered a minor breakdown, her estranged husband paid for her to visit a top psychiatrist. Since then he has seen her only occasionally, but has granted her a life of luxury with very generous alimony payments. Even though her mental state remains precarious, for the past six years she has been instrumental in setting up and running Re-Unite, a charity dedicated to helping broken and dysfunctional families. Her son Quentin is to take up the post of campaign manager in the coming weeks. The weekend gathering at Thrippleton Hall was her idea. She has never re-married.

Although Felicity receives extremely generous monthly
alimony payments from her ex-husband, the actual
amount set down in the settlement is tiny.
Every instalment is accompanied by a harsh reminder that
this excess money is paid only because of the 'extreme
generosity of Mr Orton Morton Esq. and can be
terminated at any time'.

Frank Morton
Age 54. Orton's younger brother.

Manager of one of Orton's Softee Stretchee toilet
tissue factories and junior partner in the family firm.
Trained as a book-keeper, then as an accountant, he
has worked for Orton for the past 25 years. He is a
bachelor and is considerably less flamboyant than
his brother. He is notoriously quiet and shy, evading
questions about himself, his life
and the long weekends that
he takes throughout the year
in place of conventional
holidays. He is the only
member of the family
(besides Felicity) to have
visited Quentin regularly
in prison.

Frank has always been viciously bullied by his older brother. Members of the board at Softee Stretchee were often astounded how Orton could rubbish the most sensible, well-thought-out proposals and silence his sibling just by saying 'That's enough from you, Little Frank'.

Rebecca Morton
Age 29. The elder child of Orton and Felicity Morton.

She seems to have swung to the opposite extreme from her brother, who she fought violently with as a child. Far quieter and less rebellious, she struggled through school, getting below-average grades and keeping herself to herself. For the past eleven years she has lived at home with her father, who rarely missed an opportunity to remind her how disappointing she had been to him, and has worked as a cashier in a bank in Thrippleton. She sees her mother once a year, and hadn't seen her brother for five years. She met Damien three years ago in a pub where he was performing. They announced their engagement earlier this year.

20

Rebecca was wearing extremely heavy make-up at dinner.

Her left cheek seemed to be slightly swollen.

Damien Dawson
Age 31. Rebecca Morton's boyfriend.

Employed as a garage mechanic, he dreams of
leaving the rat race behind to forge a career as a
country and western singer. So far he has not
managed to get any further than pubs and clubs
in the West Country and the slim chance of him
making a living from his music was
presumably what caused Orton to
object to the proposed marriage.
Despite having a relatively
meagre income, he enjoys
spending money on clothes,
guitars and cars.

Damien recently attacked Orton's chauffeur for 'looking at Rebecca in a suggestive way' and 'making comments' about her. The chauffeur spent a night in hospital but Orton felt calling the police would only attract unnecessary attention.

Mathilde Lefarge
Age 35. Orton Morton's lover.

A former model and beauty consultant, Mathilde met
Orton in the small 'health farm' outside Paris which
she runs. They have been together for just under two
years, although work has kept them apart for most of
that time. She was in the UK as she was looking for
suitable premises for a second health farm and hotel.
With the exception of Frank, she had
never met any of Orton's family
before the weekend of the
15th of July.

A close inspection of the telephone bill would show that someone made three short phone calls from the master bedroom, on the night of the murder, minutes before the body was discovered. Two of the calls were to France.

D.S. McGill and Quentin Morton.

Describe the events of the afternoon and evening of the 15th July.

I was picked up from HMP Whiteside by Uncle Frank at about 2pm and it took us about two and a half hours to drive down to Thrippleton. Father was out somewhere, which was the sort of warm homecoming I'd expected from him so Frank introduced me to Mathilde. I was feeling very tired so I went straight to my room...I say 'my room'...the room I had been allocated, my old room was presumably being used for something far more important, and there I slept until I was called for dinner.

One could be forgiven for thinking your prime feelings would have been of joy, of excitement. You had, after all, just been released from prison.

Have you ever been released from prison? Eighteen months inside is enough to make the outside seem fairly bizarre, coupled with the fact that all my immediate relatives seem to have suddenly remembered that I exist again. Sleep seemed to be the only option. Judging by what happened at dinner, I think it would have been better if I'd slept right through.

What did happen at dinner, exactly?

The most perfectly bloody row. I mean, as a family, and we have to go back a very long way to even find all four of us in the same room, we used to specialise in rows, but this was something special.

How did it start?

God knows. Becca started grousing about me always being served before her, or something equally trivial, then Father got all thundery, and that cretin Damien started slamming the silver around and it all kicked off. Made the mess hall at Whiteside look positively civilised.

Did you join in?

God, no. I was trying to diffuse the situation, but all their hackles were well and truly up by that stage, so it seemed fairly pointless.

What happened next?

Everybody started storming off, napkins flying all over the shop.

Who left first?

Father, as usual, growling to himself. Then Mother. No, hang on, Mathilda or whatever her name is excused herself and rushed out after Father. Then Mother, looking upset as usual, then Rebecca, then her idiot boyfriend. Me and Uncle Frank were left sitting looking at each other.

And then?

Frank shuffled off, making noises about trying to calm the situation. Snowball's chance in hell, of course, given the family's record.

And what did you do?

Me? I finished my meal alone. We didn't get much chateaubriand in Whiteside, you know. I was just helping myself to some of Mrs Beresford's trifle when all the screaming started.

When they discovered your father's body?

Yes, I suppose so. I thought it was just another little argument breaking out but then I heard Uncle Frank calling an ambulance.

How long were you alone for, before you heard the screaming?

I can't be sure exactly but I should think it was about twenty-five minutes.

That's a very specific time from someone who says they aren't sure.

After eighteen months of being locked up for 23 hours a day, one gets fairly expert at judging the passing of time.

(End of interview.)

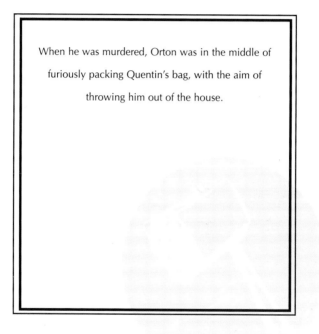

When he was murdered, Orton was in the middle of furiously packing Quentin's bag, with the aim of throwing him out of the house.

D.S. McGill and Felicity Morton.

What time did you arrive at Thrippleton Hall on the day in question?

Dinner was to be at seven thirty, so I arrived at sevenish.

Sevenish?

Yes. 'The 7 o'clock news' had just started on the radio as I turned into the drive to the house. Orton met me at the front door as I was parking and I was taken into the drawing room to meet that awful French hussy who's hanging off him at the moment.

This was the first meeting with your husband for some time. How did he seem?

Unchanged. His usual, hateful, insufferable self. He managed to be rude to everyone present before we'd finished the starter.

And how did Quentin seem after his ordeal?

Slightly subdued, at the most. Given the way he's behaved for the past ten years or so, I think a slightly subdued Quentin is a blessing for us all.

I understand that the meal was disrupted by an argument?

Yes. Rebecca, my daughter, has always had a tendency to sulk, more so when her brother is present. Orton could

never abide this. What with the significance of the
occasion, he was probably slightly on edge.

On edge?

We all were, I think. Even in the most blissfully happy
family a gathering of this size will cause certain, erm,
difficulties to arise, will cause everyone to confront the
tensions that exist between them and the family. Given the
history of our family, something like this was on the cards.
Any sort of argument, any sort of domestic violence, this
family has seen it. Tantrums, fistfights, even a stabbing with
a fork, we've seen it and done it all.

So you weren't surprised by the argument?

Not at all. We were trying to do too much at once. Meeting
ex-partners, new partners, wayward children, parents you
feel have failed you, siblings you feel at odds with, one of
these is strain enough, squashing them all together was
suicidal...er...madness. Sorry. Bad choice of word.

*When the argument heated up, who was the first
person to leave the table?*

Orton, of course, followed by that silly French girl. I went
to the bathroom.

The bathroom?

The one on the ground floor, to compose myself...

To compose yourself?

I'd forgotten just how hurtful Orton could be with a good head of steam up and how much I...we all hated him. I'd...er...I'd rather not go into the details of what he said. Now he's dead, it would be....it would be wrong to let his spitefulness live on.

When did you emerge from the bathroom?

After about ten or fifteen minutes. I'd heard lots of people thundering around, stamping up the stairs and so on. When I came back to the dining room it was completely empty, so I went off to try and find Quentin. It was his first day out of prison and it wouldn't have been fair of Orton to throw him out of the house. He needs to be given a chance. I looked in the library and was trying to get into his room, when I bumped into Orton's brother Frank. He forced open the bedroom door...and...

And?

And there he was. There was blood...blood everywhere..he was...

(The interview was terminated at this point due to Mrs Morton's distress.)

Two of the areas Felicity's psychiatrist focused on were her frequent lying, to both herself and other people, and her profound loathing of her ex-husband.

D.S. McGill and Mathilde Lefarge.

When did you arrive at Thrippleton Hall?

At about four in the afternoon. Orton said he had much work to do, so I gave myself the tour of the house and gardens.

You hadn't been there before.

No I always see...saw Orton in either Paris or London. This was being my first time out in Thrippleton. Also my first time with the family of Orton.

You've never met any of them before?

Frank only. I was a little nervous.

How did the argument at dinner start?

The children, behaving like children. The girl is...how you say?..jealous of the boy, and he is calling her a monkey and other names and Orton is on the side of his boy. A typical man, no? Then he becomes infuriated with his wife, his ex-wife, then he says something to Frank, something I don't understand it, then he leaves the table. Like a madman.

And you followed him?

Of course I follow him. I am his woman, no?

Where did he go?

Upstairs.

Where upstairs?

His...workroom, the office.

The study?

Yes, exactly. But he is so infuriated, he does not want to talk with me. He tells me to go, so I go.

Where did you go?

I go to his...to our bedroom, because naturally I am very sad, to argue with the man I love. I am there a few minutes when I hear the crying and the panic, and then...they tell me he has killed himself.

You say you spoke with him in the study, but his body was found in one of the guest bedrooms.

I do not lie to you! I speak with Orton in the study! You think I am crazy perhaps? He is the crazy man! He is cutting his neck with a knife. If a man is so crazy to do this, then he is enough crazy to walk to a different room.

I have to inform you that this is now a murder investigation, not a suicide.

Well, then, someone else is crazy! Look at this family, all of them is crazy, it is in their blood. Even this Damien, who is different family, he is also crazy.

What makes you think Damien is crazy?

After Orton tell me to go, I hear him banging and shouting 'Open bloody door! We have to sort it out now!'.

You are certain it wasn't someone else?

Of course!

How?

I know Orton's voice. Quentin has the voice of a girl, like all you posh English.

What about Frank?

Ha! You do not know Frank! Shouting is not Frank. He is like a mouse. Orton say something horrible to him, not just one thing, many things, and Frank says nothing.

And was Damien shouting and banging nearby?

Yes! It frightened me! At first I think it is Orton banging on my door but then I think this is ridiculous, because voice is different, and anyhow, I am in his bedroom, he can walk in without the banging.

Having seen photos of Thrippleton Hall, Mathilde dreamed of turning it into a high-class health farm. She told Orton this ten days ago, causing him to fly into a rage and not speak to her for two days.

D.S. McGill and Frank Morton.

What time did you arrive at Thrippleton Hall?

Well, I picked Quentin up from Whiteside, and we got back to the house at about half-four. Quentin went off to his room and I sat and read in the library until dinner.

Did anyone see you there?

No...well, er, Orton popped his head round the door at some point and we had a quick word, but apart from that, no.

There was an argument at dinner. What caused it?

Oh, Quentin, really. He was teasing his sister, who took it the wrong way.

What was he teasing her about?

Nothing. It was quite amicable. He called her 'Monkey'.

Why?

A childhood nickname, because she was always climbing and clambering over things, quite affectionate really, but she got upset by it and started sulking, which Orton has never been able to tolerate. He flew into one of his black moods and people started dropping like flies. Sorry, not a very wise choice of words there.

At what point did you leave the table?

Err, after everyone else had run away, save Quentin. I went up to see if I could calm things down at all. Without much luck, obviously.

Who did you see?

I saw Damien storming about, he seemed extremely worked up, and I saw Felicity, but only briefly.

Where was she?

In her room. Well, not her old room, a guest room. She seemed very upset. Actually she seemed upset all evening. She arrived at the dinner table after everyone else looking pale and shaky, with red puffy eyes, as if she had been crying.

How long did you spend with her?

Not very long. She's my brother's ex-wife.

So?

Well, er...Orton was very possessive and very good at leaping to the wrong conclusion, so everyone is...was...very careful about not doing anything that could be...misconstrued.

Where did you go after that?

I went to look for Rebecca. I'm quite close to the children and I thought maybe I could calm her down.

And did you find her?

No. Yes, well sort of. As I was walking down the corridor towards her bedroom, I came across Damien who was pacing up and down the corridor talking to someone in the bathroom. Assuming it was Rebecca, I turned around to go back downstairs.

But weren't you with Felicity when she discovered her ex-husband's body?

Yes. I bumped into her on my way back to the stairs after seeing Damien. She was looking for Quentin and was wrestling with the door of the guest room he was using. She seemed quite frantic, so I helped her. I put my shoulder to the door...and it opened...and there was my brother.

On the floor?

Yes. He had been slumped against the door. His weight had been holding it shut.

Did anyone else join you at the scene of the crime?

Yes. Rebecca and Damien were the first, I think. It's difficult to say, I was understandably upset. Then Mathilde came running. Then I phoned for an ambulance and the police.

Quentin?

He...er...he came upstairs soon after. He hadn't realised what had happened. He'd been downstairs throughout.

Frank has not taken a holiday for the past two years.

Instead he takes long weekends throughout the year.

Despite frequent and often cruel interrogation from Orton,

he has never revealed where he goes.

D.S. McGill and Rebecca Morton.

How did you travel to the ball?

Damien picked me up from work and we got home at about half past six. We...I went inside, went straight to my room and stayed there until dinner time. Damien...I don't know what Damien was doing. We'd had a bit of a row on the way there, you see.

I understand that there was an argument at the dinner table.

Yes. There was.

Can you tell me about it?

It was my fault, I suppose. Quentin was being horrible to me. Not very horrible, for Quentin, but I got...upset, and Daddy was angry with me. It was all silly, the same as always; Quentin being horrible, Father being angry and me getting upset.

Who was the first to leave?

Daddy.

Who was he talking to before he left the table?

He was..to everyone, really. He sort of went round everyone, wrote them off completely, with the exception of his girlfriend, and then moved onto someone else.

What did he say to your mother?

Oh, the usual rant about how pointless her charity work was, how it was 'just shutting the stable door after the horse has bolted', and how she'd never remarry, and so on.

And did this upset her?

Naturally! I mean, he was gloating, really happy, as if he was certain, or he'd seen her future or something.

Did anyone intervene?

Quentin did. Not very effectively, but he tried. He started asking Uncle Frank about what he'd been up to, what he'd been doing with his free time, and Frank began to answer, and then Daddy started leering at him, saying 'Yes, what have you been doing?' and calling him 'Little Frank'. It was awful, it really was.

What happened then?

Quentin weighed in, telling him to go steady or to ease up or something, and Daddy exploded, calling him ungrateful and a waste of space, then he stormed out.

You left the room as well.

Yes...I was very upset and I went upstairs to the bathroom.

Why not your bedroom?

I...er...I didn't feel very well.

And you were in there until they found your father?

Yes.

Did you speak to Damien while you were in there?

Oh...I didn't realise...I'm...

It's just that he was heard hammering on a door and telling someone to unlock it.

Yes, he was quite angry, because he was worried. He shouted 'Open the bloody door. We have to sort this out!'

Did you open the door?

No, but he calmed down and was whispering through the door. Then I heard Mummy scream, and I came out and we went there together.

What was the argument about?

It's a very personal thing.

This is a very serious incident.

I'm...it's just that...I'd just discovered I'm pregnant.

And Damien was angry about this?

No...Damien was overjoyed...it...

You don't want the baby?

Of course I want the baby. It's not that...it was an accident...and...

And?

(silence)

And?

Daddy found the test kit...he was furious...he said that he was going to make me get rid of it and then he was going to get rid of Damien, and that I was a slut...and...

(Interview terminated due to extreme distress of interviewee.)

Rebecca has felt sick and nauseous throughout the three months she has been pregnant. Damien has picked her up from work and driven her home to Thrippleton Hall most evenings and, much to Orton's annoyance, stayed for dinner each night.

D.S. McGill and Damien Dawson.

On the afternoon in question, what time did you arrive at Thrippleton Hall?

After work, so about half six. I picked Becky up from the bank at just after half five, we came back via Thrippleford Priors, cos I had to give a quote on a faulty transmission to one of my cousins there, got up to the Hall about half six. Becky went and had a lie-down, cos she was tired.

What did you do?

Watched a bit of telly. Then went out to the drive, tinkered around with the car. Becky's mum came out, asked if I could check the electrics in her Saab. She said neither the windows nor the stereo was working. I said I didn't have the right kit with me, but I told her I'd look at it when I was next up. Then she went back into the house to look for Orton and I carried on tinkering until dinner.

And how was that?

Oh, you know, the usual. Lots of shouting, lots of tears. I mean, they're all horrible to each other, that family, and I know I'm biased but they all seem particularly horrible to Becky. It's little things, she knows they're only little, but they still upset her.

How did the argument start?

Like I said, just niggly little things. That Quentin being a brat. You'd think that prison would have knocked it out of him, but there he was, winding everyone up. Then it all snowballed. People storming out and such. When Becky left the table, I went to look for her.

Where was she?

In the upstairs bathroom.

And you went straight there?

Yes. I was worried about her.

How did you know she'd be there?

I...well, I looked in her room and she wasn't there, so I tried the bathroom...

You were heard shouting 'Open this bloody door! Let's sort this out once and for all'.

She'd locked herself in.

It's quite an aggressive thing to shout to someone you're worried about, isn't it?

Erm...

Isn't it?

I...er...I guess I was just a bit wound up, you know, the atmosphere, everyone shouting and that.

Did she open the door?

Only after Mrs Morton started screaming. There was a loud crash, which was Frank kicking the door in, then lots of screaming.

Did you see Mr Morton at all on your search for Rebecca?

No. The door to the guest bedroom was closed when I went past.

But wouldn't you have expected him to be in his study, or his own bedroom, rather than one of the guest rooms?

Er...yeah....I suppose so.

So why did you say that the door to the guest bedroom was shut?

Well...er... that's where they found him wasn't it?
So he must have been in there when I went past.

Twice a week Damien swaps his spanners and overalls for a stetson and guitar, performing country and western under the pseudonym of Duane Derby. This is an extract from his song 'I Love My Girl (But I Wanna Kill Her Daddy)'.

Now I don't look for trouble,
I'm a peaceful kinda guy,
But if ol' trouble calls me,
I'll look him in the eye.
Because I love my sweetheart,
I try to love her family,
But her daddy, he don't like me,
so he's trouble with a capital T.
Ol' trouble he don't want me to
make his girl my wife,
So unless he can try and change his mind,
I guess I'll have to take his life.

Plan of Study

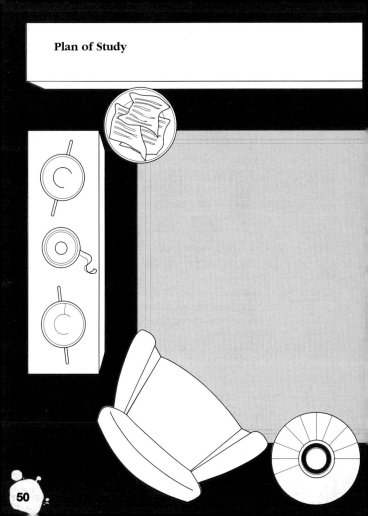

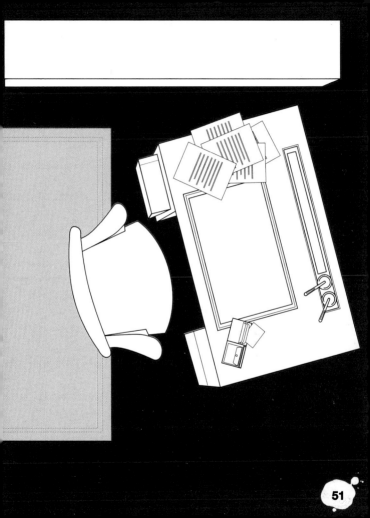

Orton Morton's study has always been his 'den' and his place of sanctuary. It is full of awards of excellence for his company's products and in an illuminated display cabinet down one wall of the study, he has a gold-plated toilet roll mounted on a stand, which he lovingly polishes each day. Every single member of the family knows if you enter the study, you do so at your own risk. Even Mrs Beresford needs to get special permission to go in every Saturday morning and clean the room.

53

notes

DS McGill's Notes

Something very fishy going on here.

Can see possible motive for all immediate family members as victim seems to have been a bit of a tyrant (to do: establish character profile of Orton). Nothing concrete for any of them.

Two non-family members: no immediate motive established as yet, but both seemed particularly uneasy/suspicious on interview.

No one emerges as chief suspect, but there seem to be holes in everyone's argument.

e.g. Quentin Morton claims he waited in dining room until after the body was discovered, but his mother says it was empty when she went past. (to do: establish where everyone was sitting, maybe he was in the room but obscured).

Felicity Morton: 7 o'clock news (to do: check with Damien Dawson whether her car stereo was working or not).

Mathilde Lefarge: only one to hold to suicide story. Study? (to do: forensic to do complete check on Orton's study).

Frank Morton: 'bumped into' Felicity Morton.

Rebecca Morton: Both Frank Morton and Damien Dawson went to
look for her, but only Damien found her, didn't actually see her.

Damien Dawson: witnesses heard him being very aggressive.

If Orton left study for bedroom being used by Quentin Morton, how
come no one saw him leave, as all except Quentin were running
around upstairs?

Also, unless murderer went through window, someone would
probably have seen him/her go in (to do: establish exactly what
everyone was doing around landing/study/bedroom).

notes

notes

Scene of Crime Report 2

The study, first floor, Thrippleton Hall.

No direct sign of struggle.
The desk drawer was open and a wallet (identified as belonging to the deceased) was lying open on top, with a credit card (also belonging to the deceased) sticking out of one of the pockets.
Fingerprinting revealed prints, other than those of the victim on the card.

Two crumpled sheets of personalised note paper (also belonging to the deceased) were found in the bin.
The first was addressed to the board of directors of Softee Stretchee, announcing the removal of Frank Morton from both the general manager's position at the Scunthorpe factory and his seat on the board, on the grounds of 'gross professional misconduct'.
The second was a letter to Maculloch, Sergeant and Pattinson, the firm of solicitors who have acted for the deceased for the past two decades, instructing them to cease all payments to the deceased's ex-wife above and beyond the minimum outlined in the divorce settlement.
No reason was given for this.
The handwriting has been identified as that of the victim. On both documents were prints belonging to someone other than the victim. Although it is difficult to say from the poor quality of the prints, they appear to be different to those on the credit card.

Mathilde was convicted for fraud when she was nineteen. She was found guilty of forging her ageing grandmother's signature on an amendment to the old lady's life assurance, making Mathilde the sole beneficiary. An impassioned plea from the old lady, who had bitterly regretted informing on her granddaughter, saved Mathilde from prison. The old lady died three weeks later when her brand new car span out of control and hit a brick wall.

Morton's credit card bill, requested by D.S. McGill.

MASTER CHARGE
CREDIT CARD BILL

Account name: O L Morton

Account number: 4343 6784 2312

Statement date: 18th July

Date   4 JULY
Transactions   MORGANS VINTNERS
Debits/Credit   £416.78D

Date   4 JULY
Transactions   SETTERS BESPOKE
Debits/Credit   £614.00D

Date   8 JULY
Transactions   CLARIDGES
Debits/Credit   £120.00D

Date   15 JULY
Transactions   PAN AM 1st CLASS SINGLE TO PARIS
Debits/Credit   £219.00D

Date   15 JULY
Transactions   HOTEL CHI-CHI
Debits/Credit   Ffr 3,100D

Date   15 JULY
Transactions   VOITURE DE STYLE
Debits/Credit   Ffr 2,499D

The solid-silver 18th century fruit knife that killed Orton had been placed on the serving table in the dining room by Mrs Beresford that morning. When questioned by the police, she said she had noticed a couple of other items of silverware were missing before dinner, but when they went together to the library to check them, they had reappeared. But she said that when she had checked the serving table immediately before dinner, the knife was in place.

Snatches of the argument at dinner, overheard by Mrs Beresford.

Quentin:
Can you pass me the spuds, please, Monkey?

Rebecca:
Don't call me 'Monkey'!

Orton:
Ha! I haven't heard anyone call you that for years!

Felicity:
Orton, you know she hates be...

Orton:
Oh for God's sake, woman! It's only a bit of fun. She's an adult, she should be able to look after herself.

Felicity:
Quentin, apologise to your sister immediately!

Orton:
He's just come out of bloody prison! He's not...

Felicity:
Quentin!

Quentin:
I'm sorry. I didn't mean to tease you.....Monkey.

(sound of knife and fork being slammed down)

Felicity:
Stop it! Make him stop!

Orton (shouts):
How dare you shout at the table! The pair of you! Bloody women!

(at this point Mrs Beresford retreated to a safe distance. About five minutes later she returned to hear the following exchange.)

Orton:
....and frankly, I can't believe that I ever found you attractive. The fact that I went as far as to actually marry you is a source of constant bewilderment to me.

(Awkward silence. Faint sobbing could be heard.)

Quentin (clearing his throat):
So tell me Uncle Frank, what have you been up to while I was enjoying Her Majesty's hospitality?

Orton (aside):
Ho ho, this should be interesting!

Frank:
Well, er, nothing much, you know. Just trundling along.

Quentin (amicably):
You must have done something!

Orton:
Yes, little brother, what have you been up to? All those weekends away, shrouded in secrecy. Judging by what I've seen today, you've been very naughty. Come on, Little Frank, what have you been up to?

Quentin:
Father, leave Uncle Frank alone!

Orton:
*Don't use that tone with me, your own father! I just want
him to answer your question boy.*

Quentin:
*You are without doubt my father but at least Frank had
the decency to turn up to my trial and to visit me while I
was inside.*

Orton (exploding):

(slamming of cutlery and scraping of chair)

*Of all the ungrateful, spoilt little brats! You waste the
most expensive education money can buy, you waste
your youth with pot-heads and hippies, giving a two-
finger salute to everything I've given you and then when
your good-for-nothing friends land you in a spot of
bother, you want me to wipe your nose for you. Obviously
a bit of prison wasn't enough for you, was it? Well, let's
see how you do out on your own. The whole bloody lot
of you!*

(Mrs Beresford retreats hastily as Orton storms out of the
room, leaving a stunned silence in his wake.)

DS McGill's Notes

Mental cruelty seems sufficient motive for immediate family.

All seem unstable/dysfunctional.

Rebecca Morton/Damien Dawson: Orton was considerable obstacle

to future happiness.

Mathilde Lefarge: previous record? Gold digger? Incident with

grandmother?

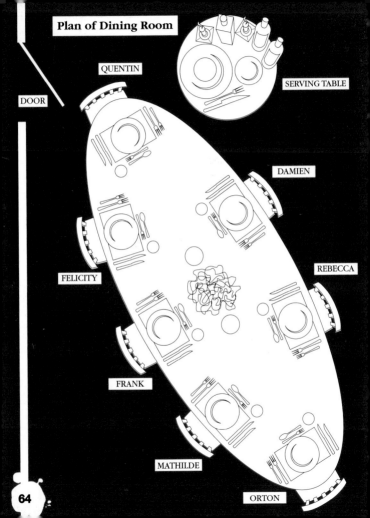

Plan of Dining Room

QUENTIN

DOOR

SERVING TABLE

DAMIEN

FELICITY

REBECCA

FRANK

MATHILDE

ORTON

64

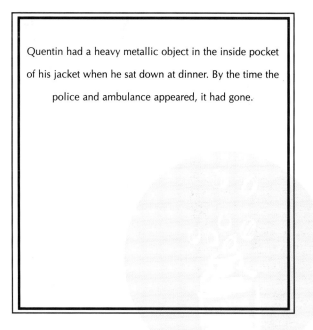

Quentin had a heavy metallic object in the inside pocket of his jacket when he sat down at dinner. By the time the police and ambulance appeared, it had gone.

The Surgery

THRIPPLETON UPPERS

19th July

Dear DS McGill,

Thank you for your enquiry regarding the Morton family's health records. Orton himself had not been near the surgery for many years, preferring someone on Harley Street. Likewise, Felicity and Quentin have been away from the village for some time, for various reasons. Frank has a fairly healthy constitution and so Rebecca is the only member of the family with whom I've had regular contact.

The majority of her ailments have been trivial, perhaps even unnecessary but sadly I feel I have to say that I've noticed signs of trauma in her, since a disturbingly early age.

My records, going back over more than 25 years, show that on four occasions she has come to me with unrelated complaints, but with visible facial bruising. When questioned, she declined to give me any details of the injuries.

In general discussions, she has often seemed unhappy and, on occasions, quite profoundly depressed. She seemed extremely unhappy at home, feeling isolated and cut off from her father, who she always seemed extremely reluctant to discuss.

Recently she came to see me, again reticently, with various questions concerning motherhood. She seemed both anxious and gloomy.

I am sorry not to be of more help regarding other family members and that what I did have to contribute is not really very positive. Please do not hesitate to contact me if you have any further questions.

Yours sincerely

V Rosler

Dr U Rosler

D.S. McGill and Mathilde Lefarge,
conducted at her insistence.

The subject seemed very distressed, and insisted on speaking to DS McGill, despite him being off duty at the time.

I understand you have something to add to your previous statement.

Yes, I have. I have to tell you that before I lied.

What did you lie about?

Before, I said that I left the table and I go to talk with Orton in his study, but this is not true.

What is the truth then?

I went up the stairs and I hear Orton shut the door to his study very strongly. But then I go to the bedroom.

So you didn't talk to him?

No. He was so infuriated. I have never seen him like this. I was scared.

Did you stay in the bedroom?

No.

What did you do?

A bad thing. A very bad thing.

What?

I heard him go out of the study into another room.

Which room?

The room where Quentin is staying. And I go into the study, very quietly, and I take his purse from the drawers and I take his American Express card and I go back to the bedroom.

And what did you do there?

I take the card and I buy a ticket to France.

Anything else?

Yes, a hotel room and a car to pick me up at the airport.

Why did you do this?

This is very difficult for me....For two years now, I know Orton. He is a very generous man, but he is...cold. To begin with I think this is the famous English reserve, but then...he never introduce me to his family until now, and then...bouf...I see why. He is little Napoleon. I see how he treats his children, and I think, these children are a little...how do you say?...odd. But then I see how he treat Felicity, and I think...

What did you think?

That this man is a monster! So I think 'No!' and I decide to leave.

That's a very dramatic decision.

I am a woman and I am French. I have intuition; I feel something, I do it.

You also have a previous conviction for fraud.

That was a long time ago. Maybe what I did was wrong, but I was scared. And something else. When I am going from the bedroom to the study to get the card, I see that Damien, and what I said I heard him shouting, he was shouting at the door of Quentin's room.

At Orton?

Yes! 'Open this door! We have to bloody sort out this!', or something like that.

You're certain about this? You've lied before.

No! This is truth. I promise you!

Did the door open?

I don't know. I wait till it is all quiet before I go back to the bedroom.

And did you see anyone in the corridor when you took the credit card back to the study?

No, but just after I returned to the bedroom I heard footsteps and then.... how you say?...... raised voices and then screaming......

HMP Whiteside
Hospital Wing

PSYCHIATRIC ASSESSMENT

Subject: Morton Quentin D'Arby Forbes
WHS445120/6

Status: Prior to Release

Offence(s): Accessory to Armed Robbery

Assessor: Dr Jeanette Williams

Release Date: 15.07.96

Report:
In addition to a multiple substance abuse problem (primarily heroin, alcohol running a close second), the subject displayed on admission classic symptoms of a sociopathic personality, occasionally bordering on psychosis. Most sociopaths display an ignorance of authority; this subject seemed to go a step further, hating it in all its manifestations. This hatred seems to have been rooted in problems with his father as a child, compounded by the replacement of a father-figure with boarding school at age six. All of this was aggravated by the refusal of subject's father to act as character witness at trial. He has made incredible progress since admission, responding to treatment in an exceptional way. Some assessors (notably Dr Smithers) expressed doubt as to the validity of this miraculous turnaround, but generally feedback from sources both in the medical wing and outside was so positive as to prompt early re-admission into society.
A job well-done!

FRAMPTONSHIRE CONSTABULARY

Thrippleton Police Station

M E M O

FROM: DS McGILL
DATE: 20th July
RE: VICTIM PROFILE OF ORTON MORTON

ESTABLISHING VALID PROFILE OF THE DECEASED HAS
PROVED VIRTUALLY IMPOSSIBLE.
FAMILY WILL SAY ONLY THAT THEY NEVER WANTED FOR
ANYTHING.
COLLEAGUES COMMENTED ON HIS APPETITE FOR HARD
WORK AND HIS ACUTE BUSINESS SENSE.
FAILED TO FIND ANYONE WHO WOULD CLASSIFY
THEMSELVES AS HIS 'FRIEND'.
EMPLOYEES ALL REFUSED TO SAY ANYTHING ON THE
RECORD. ONE SOURCE DID CONTRIBUTE THE FOLLOWING,
BUT THEN HAD SECOND THOUGHTS AND REFUSED TO PUT
HIS NAME TO IT:
'HE WAS A RUTHLESS BUSINESSMAN WHO SEEMED TO
TAKE REAL DELIGHT IN TAKING REVENGE ON ANYONE
WHO CROSSED HIM, BE THEY EMPLOYEES, BUSINESS
CONTACTS OR CORPORATE RIVALS. IN ONE CASE SOFTEE
STRETCHEE TOOK OVER A DOG BISCUIT FACTORY, ONLY
TO SELL IT FOR SCRAP AT A LOSS OF £3.4M.
RUMOUR HAD IT THAT THE ONLY REASON MORTON
COMPLETED THE DEAL WAS BECAUSE HE WAS CONVINCED
THAT THE BLOKE WHO OWNED IT HAD CHEATED IN A
ROUND OF GOLF. 'I FOR ONE AM GLAD THAT HE IS
DEAD.'

HMP Whiteside
Hospital Wing

PSYCHIATRIC ASSESSMENT

INTERNAL MEMO

To: Dr Jeanette Williams

From: Dr Norman Smithers

Date: 14th July

Regarding: Final Assessment on Morton, QDF WHS445120/6

It is very rare I find cause to question the work of a colleague, let alone a superior and significantly more experienced one, so it is with regret that I find myself compelled to strongly disagree with much of what I read in the report on the above prisoner. In my opinion, based on numerous one-to-one sessions, Morton is a cunning, manipulative and far-from-reformed character. More significantly, given his early release, he is an individual capable of much harm to those around him. I can only conclude that his early release, coupled with the vainglorious tone of the report, is a grave error and one that I wish to publicly distance myself from, both professionally and personally.

Yours regretfully

B G Smithers

Dr   B G Smithers

D.S. McGill and Damien Dawson.

(The subject seemed nervous and unsettled.)

A couple of things have cropped up since we last spoke.

Like what?

Well, there seems to be a discrepancy in your...

A what?

I have reason to believe that your previous story isn't completely true. We have a witness who says that she saw you hammering on the door of the guest bedroom, not the bathroom as you claimed in your previous account.

Er...

Is this true?

Well..yes, but that doesn't prove anything.

Who did you think was inside?

I don't know.

Did you think it was Rebecca?

I don't know.

***So you go around shouting aggressively at anyone,
do you?***

It was Orton.

How do you know?

I saw him go in. I tried to speak to him, civil-like, when he
was on his way in, but he just ignored me, like he always
did.

What did you want to 'sort out'?

The whole thing. The way he treats Becky, the way he treats
me, it's just not right. I'd been trying to talk to Becky, who'd
locked herself in the bathroom but she wasn't answering
cos she was so upset, and then I got a bit worked up, and
went to find Orton. Faced with a second locked door in as
many minutes, I just sort of lost my rag a bit. Started hitting
the door and shouting and that. It's not like me. Honest it
isn't.

How did Orton respond to this?

He didn't. There was a lot of shuffling, before I shouted,
then it all went quiet. The moment I had done it, I regretted
it, so I went back to try to talk to Becky. Like I told you the
first time, she didn't say anything to me, not for ages. They
can be awkward sods, these Mortons.

How long were you there for?

She didn't say anything to me for about ten minutes or so.

Nothing at all?

No. I heard her opening the window and having a wash, but it was probably about ten minutes before she said anything to me. Then she told me how she was sorry for running off and how she should be used to her dad by now and how it would all be different when we're married. Then all the commotion started and we both went to see what was going on.

Rebecca as well?

She heard her mum screaming and was off like a shot.

So why did you lie?

I...I didn't want you to think that it was me what done it. I didn't think anyone had seen me, so I thought it was a bit of a white lie. Becky heard me for all but a minute or so, she'll tell you it wasn't me.

notes

DS McGill's Notes.

Was knife already in Quentin Morton's bedroom?

If not, who could have picked it up on way out of the dining room?

Mathilde Lefarge: plans to return to France = escape route?

Access to bedroom seems to be key to whodunit.

Landing like Piccadilly Circus before/during crime.

Virtually everybody was seen by someone else.

Possible for killer to enter room unseen?

Laboratory tests found traces of saliva on the handle of

the antique silver fruit knife which was used as the murder weapon.

D.S. McGill and Frank Morton.

*Returning to the argument at dinner, Orton asked
you to say what you'd 'been up to'. To what do you
think he was referring?*

Er..about...my social life....you know...just a friendly
enquiry.

*But I've been told that there seemed to be something
malicious about the question.*

That's just...my brother's manner.

*Are you also aware that your brother's final act was
to dismiss you from your job and from the board?*

No...God...no.

*At the same time he cut off virtually all payments to
his ex-wife. Have you any idea why he would do
that?*

Er...no...no I don't.

Would there be any connection between the two?

(silence)

Mr Morton?

My brother...this afternoon, I was, er, talking to Felicity in the library. Orton walked in, and then walked out again. He must have got the wrong idea.

Hence your desire not to be 'caught' by your brother later on that evening?

Exactly.

Did anyone else see you in the library?

Yes. I might as well come completely clean. I saw Quentin. I didn't mention it before, because he seemed to be...

Yes?

He seemed to be stealing some of the silverware from the dining room. Felicity didn't see, she had her back to him, so I kept quiet. I caught his eye and he sneaked off.

Did you see what he was carrying?

I think he had one of the candlesticks.

Did you go into the study at any point that evening?

No. The afternoon was the only part I lied about. I just didn't want...to cause Felicity any embarrassment, particularly at a time like this. The evening part is all exactly as I told you. Honestly.

All the silverware, bar the murder weapon, was found to be in place when Mrs Beresford checked with the police, although she had noticed the candlestick missing before dinner. Did you mention anything to Quentin?

No, but he knew that I'd seen him. Hopefully he thought better of it and put it back.

Mrs Beresford noticed an empty bottle of scotch on the serving table when she checked for the silverware. Did you drink it?

No, I don't usually drink scotch. Quentin's part of Narcotics Anonymous so he's not supposed to drink. He was abstinent at dinner, so I don't think it was him. I hope it wasn't him. Maybe it was Damien?

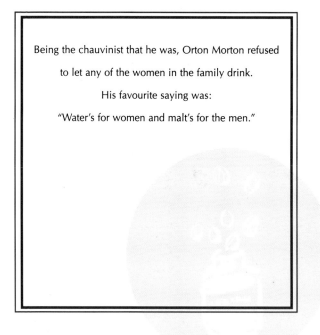

Being the chauvinist that he was, Orton Morton refused

to let any of the women in the family drink.

His favourite saying was:

"Water's for women and malt's for the men."

Overheard conversation between Frank and Quentin.

Frank:
I saw you take that silver, you know.

Quentin:
And I saw you with Mother. Tut tut, Uncle Frank.

Frank:
Your mother is already extremely upset. You don't want to upset her any more, do you?

Quentin:
Well as long as you don't tell the police about the silverware...

Frank:
I already have.

Quentin:
You what? Are you mad? I'm on bloody parole in case you hadn't realised!

Frank:
I had to. You see, your father also saw us.

Quentin:
Well, no wonder he was so wound up. Still, no reason to get the police onto me. After all, I put it all back.

Frank:
They're more worried about the murder weapon.

Quentin:
Well I didn't touch it. I just took a couple of candlesticks.

Frank:
What for?

Quentin:
To sell, I'm penniless and Father wouldn't miss them. Anyhow, after you saw, I thought better of it and put everything back.

Frank:
All of it?

Quentin:
Yes! I had the last candlestick in my pocket at dinner. I put it back when everyone ran off.

Frank:
You didn't tell the police that though, did you?

Quentin:
I...I had a couple of drinks you see. I put it back, and there were all these bottles on the table..and I...had a few drinks.

Frank:
Why didn't you tell the police?

Quentin:
Well, I'm not supposed to...if the shrinks find out they'll revoke my parole.

Frank:

But you're certain you didn't touch the knife? You didn't leave it in your room?

Quentin:

Look, that knife is worth a fraction of those big candlesticks, or those goblets, or half the things hanging around this old heap.

Frank:

You're sure about this?

Quentin:

Yes, I know my standing isn't that high at the moment and I know I had my differences with Dad, but I wouldn't kill him. I didn't kill him.

Frank:

Of course you didn't, Quentin, of course you didn't.

Quentin:

Look, if you don't believe me ask Mrs B.

Frank:

Mrs Beresford?

Quentin:

Yes. She caught me red-handed, bottle to my lips. She gave me the works. You know, about how she changed my nappy and what a sweet child I was and what was I doing with my life. But I made her promise not to tell the police, so you mustn't drop her in it. Please don't Uncle Frank, she was so sweet about it.

DS McGill's Notes.

Quentin Morton. Has long-standing motive (but then so do all the rest), stole silver (but did return it, and knew that he'd been seen) also had opportunity to take knife from serving table without being discovered, however, no-one saw him upstairs (to do: confront Quentin Morton with apparent lie).

Rebecca Morton and Damien Dawson: Rebecca must have lied about Damien hammering on bathroom door to protect him. Still, no real reason to suspect she's still lying. Not seen or heard outside bathroom.

Felicity Morton: has lied about both before and after dinner. Maybe lying about Quentin not being in dining room. Together with Frank, has best motive. Presumably one or both of them destroyed letters in the study. But murderer much more careful than this.

Scene of crime: damaged hinges? - if from discovery, then body

fell against door? How did killer leave? Maybe suicide after all?

Murder weapon: must have been picked up in mass exodus from

dining room; by who? (to do: look again at seating plan and ask

Quentin Morton if he'd stolen it and left it in suitcase in room).

Saliva: how did saliva get on knife handle? why? bit of a mystery -

(to do: DNA tests from all six suspects; a positive identification

might well point to the murderer as no one has so far admitted

seeing or touching the knife).

CONCLUSION

Here end the rather messy files of DS McGill.
They contain all the necessary information to identify
the murderer, as well as several false clues and dead
ends. It's time to decide whodunit but before you turn
over, think of your promotion and your reputation,
both of which depend on your ability to solve this
crime.

Check through your notes carefully, comparing them
to those of DS McGill.

(The first solution page is in mirror-writing, to stop an
accidental glance ruining the book - hold the book up
to a mirror when you turn the page, and all will be
revealed!)

DON'T TURN THE PAGE-

unless you want to know the solution!

SOLUTION

Rebecca Morton was the murderer.

Her motive: years of parental cruelty (physical as well as mental; the bruise on her face was the result of a clash with Orion) made her desperately miserable and dangerously unstable. Her father's refusal to permit her to start a family with Damien, let alone give the relationship his blessing, was enough to make her realise drastic steps would have to be taken. She had meant to leave the Hall to set up home with her fiancé, but the argument at dinner was the straw that broke the camel's back.

PROCESS OF DEDUCTION:

All the suspects had possible motives for killing the deceased:

Frank Morton had been having an illicit affair with Orton's ex-wife for some time (hence the secrecy surrounding his whereabouts on long weekends) and he was bullied mercilessly by his brother but he had an alibi in Felicity (and we know that the murderer acted alone). When Frank left the dining room, he went up to Felicity's room to check she was OK after she had arrived late for dinner looking as if she had been crying and after Orton's verbal attack on her during dinner. Despite playing it down to DS McGill, he spent some time with her, before going to check up on Rebecca. After seeing Damien talking to someone in the bathroom, who he assumed was Rebecca, Frank went back towards the stairs, as he told DS McGill. In doing so, he bumped into Felicity trying to get into the guest room Quentin was using. He forced the door open (hence the damaged hinges) and together they found Orton Morton's dead body.
Frank was telling the truth when he said that he had no idea about being sacked.

Felicity Morton had reason to kill her former husband because not only did she hate him but she had found out that he was going to cut her alimony payments back to the bare minimum required by law, yet she had an alibi in Frank.

She was late for dinner and arrived pale and shaky because she had been destroying the letters she had found in her husband's study, where she had gone in search of him before dinner in an attempt to counsel him on how to handle the family gathering. Throwing away the letters was a foolish action which Orton, had he lived, would have discovered immediately and which, if clear fingerprints were found on the paper, would have made Felicity the chief murder suspect.

A compulsive liar and keen to hide her involvement with Frank, she lied to DS McGill about the time of her arrival at the Hall (her car stereo was not working, according to Damien, so how could she have been listening to the News?). She also lied about her movements after leaving the dinner table. She did not go to the downstairs bathroom, nor did she enter the library or return to the dining room (otherwise she would have seen Quentin), instead she fled sobbing to the sanctuary of her room, where she was followed by Frank. When Frank went in search of Rebecca, Felicity went to check up on Quentin, who she assumed was in his bedroom.

Mathilde Lefarge had a motive to kill Orton in that she wanted to convert the Hall into a health farm. She didn't have an alibi but we know she must have been in the master bedroom making the phone calls which she would have had to make in order to buy an airline ticket, reserve a hotel room and hire a car to pick her up from the airport (see credit card bill).

She was guilty only of paying for her flight, hotel and car with Orton's credit card, which she stole from his wallet, which she found in his study. The attempted fraud in her teens was her only fumbling entrée into the world of crime. Her grandmother's death was no more than an accident.

The key to the murder was access to the knife, which we know was on the serving table in the dining room before dinner, and access to Quentin's room.

From looking at the seating plan we can deduce that Damien, Rebecca and Quentin could have picked up the knife on their way out of the dining room; the others were unlikely to have passed the serving table on their way to the door.

Damien Dawson was very possessive of Rebecca and could have wanted to kill Orton because of his treatment of her, but he has an alibi.

Although he saw no one except Orton (entering the guest room which Quentin was using) after leaving the dining room, he was seen pacing up and down outside the bathroom by Frank and outside the guest room, shouting at Orton by Mathilde.

Quentin Morton could have wanted to kill Orton as he was very angry that he had not turned up at his trial nor had his father visited him in prison. He didn't have an alibi, **BUT. . .**

He was busy returning the silver to the serving table (we know it was missing before dinner, and Frank had pointed the finger at Quentin, yet it had been replaced by the time the police arrived). He also drank the whisky and was caught and lectured to by Mrs Beresford. Had he gone upstairs, it is likely that someone would have seen him with all the comings and goings in the corridors.

He is trying to 'go straight', despite the damning report from Dr Smithers, who has since been suspended suffering from 'profound psychotic negativity'.

Rebecca Morton, on the other hand, picked the knife up from the serving table as she left the dining room. She went to the bathroom as she claimed, locked the door, climbed out the window and, with the fruit knife firmly clenched between her teeth (hence the saliva), crossed the balcony to the guest room, her childhood 'monkey' climbing talents coming into play.

Inside the guest room, Orton was furiously packing Quentin's things with the intention of throwing him out of the house. When Rebecca climbed in through the unlocked window, he didn't see the knife and made a point of ignoring what he presumed was a childish prank, allowing her to cut his throat with relative ease, just as Damien finished hammering on the door demanding to talk to him. Rebecca then crept back along the ledge and climbed back in through the bathroom window. She closed the window and washed the blood off her hands (this is what Damien heard through the closed door, having returned to the bathroom from outside the guest room).

All this took Rebecca around 10 minutes - the time period Damien told DS McGill it took Rebecca to respond to his questioning through the locked door.
When Felicity's screams were heard, Rebecca was 'off like a shot' as she knew what had happened and where everyone was gathered.

As Orton's body was found collapsed against the bedroom door, the murderer could not have left the room by the door. He or she could not have entered by the door either as, according to Damien, it was locked (Orton had locked the door behind him so no-one could try and persuade him to change his mind about throwing Quentin out of the house). The killer must therefore have entered and left the guest room via the balcony, which goes along outside the room to the bathroom on one side and a guest room on the other. As the guest room was vacant and locked the murderer must have gained access to the balcony via the bathroom.